D1094656

The Loggers

How They Saw It

© 2010 Written by Charles A. Rollins

Edited and Published by Kizzar Publishing
October 2010, First Edition in Series

Printed and bound by TJ Int'l Istanbul, Turkey

International Standard Book Number 978-0615-33533-9

Special Thanks

I would like to express my appreciation to all those who helped make this book possible.

Lew & Mona Roberts, Sandy Cartisser, Steve & Judy Lehl, Scott Sloan, Bill Carr, Norm Smith, Heather Mundle, Marie & Robin Kizzar.

To all the old time loggers who shared their stories with me.

Cliff Graff, Bill Birkenfield, Milt Warren, Chuck Pierce, Raymond Smith, Joy Englhart, Allen Baker, Jim Baker, Frank Dunlap, Al Kimbley, and to the many loggers who I've crossed paths with.

THANKS GUYS!

Forward

As a logging historian and ex-timber faller, I have had the privilege of working and talking with many old time loggers. Sharing their stories with me and seeing the pride they showed in their faces when they talked about the good old days has led me to compile this book honoring their legacy. The photo postcards and stories used in this book are not all inclusive but provide a perspective of the logging industry at the turn of the century as seen through the logger's eyes. After giving a historical presentation a prominent historian said something I have never forgotten, "As historians we have to get it right!" Every effort has been made to be as accurate as possible in documenting this period of logging history.

Over time we tend to forget our past. As most of the big trees are gone, my desire was to put together a book of memories in a pictorial format documenting the loggers way of life. If a picture is worth a thousand words then let these picture postcards be the loggers words in telling their stories.

This book is dedicated to the men and women who worked the forest of the Pacific Northwest, since it was their passion for their logging heritage that made this book possible.

Introduction

At the turn of the century Douglas fir covered much of the Pacific Northwest. Western red cedar, hemlock, spruce and pine were very abundant. These trees held some of the finest lumber that could be found anywhere in the world. The forest was wild and rugged with steep mountains, deep valleys and many large rivers and streams. The trees were so thick it was difficult to walk through them and it seemed to rain non-stop. Due to the vastness of the region, the pioneers that settled in Oregon and Washington faced many challenges. Trees needed to be cut and cleared so they could work the land. The loggers were experienced woodsmen known to get the job done and who were not afraid to face these challenges. Well respected, these men were called upon to harvest the trees and build the roads that were needed. Resourceful, the loggers were always looking for a faster and cheaper way to get the job done.

They were called "timber beast, lumberjack and logger". It took a special breed of men to work the forest. Someone willing to work from dawn to dusk in all types of weather. Some of the terrain was so steep you needed to be half Billy goat. The work was hard and dangerous and a man had to be tough. Coming from all walks of life, the early loggers gained a great deal of experience as they worked the timber from the East Coast to the Midwest gradually working their way to the Pacific Northwest. Many of the loggers brought their families with them and began building homes, schools, stores and churches. Some of these logging settlements would grow into the communities of today and over time some have faded away. The loggers all had the same goal in common. They were willing to work hard under primitive and tough conditions so their families could live the American Dream.

In 1906 Eastman-Kodak began selling the autographic camera that used a picture postcard format. The camera was compact and lightweight, easy to use. The back of the camera had a small hatch that could be opened allowing the user to write identifying comments right on the negative. After a picture was taken and developed it would come back as a photo postcard. On the back of the card a message could be written and for just one cent, mailed anywhere in the United States. Loggers loved to have their pictures taken so it didn't take long for the camera to make its way into the woods. With camera in hand, the loggers started taking pictures by the thousands showing what they did and how they did it. The authentic photo postcards in this book are snapshots in time showing how the loggers and their families lived and saw life a century ago. Many of these postcards were mailed to family members and friends around the country. Over time most were lost or discarded.

It was at a local flea market in 1977 when I purchased my first real photo logging postcard. Discovering that the picture was taken by the loggers themselves made those photos more unique, the search was on, leaving no stone unturned if there was a chance of finding a great image. Thirty-three years later I have acquired a nice collection of these real photo postcards covering many of the early logging activities of the timber industry from 1906 to the late 1920's. The views showing the falling and bucking of the trees, pulling the logs out of the forest and then getting them to the mill are all authentic. Most of the photo postcards are one of a kind, for they were taken by the loggers themselves. Professional photographers did go into the woods to take photos for the logging operation to sell at their studios and local markets. I have used a few professional photo postcards but only when there was no other image available.

The Fallers

The Fallers

Three boards high, fallers standing on springboards, chopping the face in the tree in the direction they wanted it to fall.

The Northwest timber was large and tall, three feet to as much as sixteen feet in diameter and 150 to around 300 feet tall. Cutting these massive trees was a real art. The fallers or choppers took great pride in making the tree fall where they wanted it to go. It was the fallers job to cut the tree down with as little breakage as possible and in a way so the logs could be pulled or yarded out of the woods after the tree was bucked. There was an old saying that "you fall the tree toward the mill" but you had to go by the lay of the land and the lean of the tree.

The tools of the trade included a falling saw 8 to 12 feet long. These saws were thinner than a bucking saw and more flexible making it easier to pull the saw through the tree. Springboards were wooden planks inserted into slots cut into the base of the tree used like a platform so the fallers could work above the swell of the tree. A falling axe was razor sharp and would penetrate deep into the tree making large chips fly with each swing. Steel wedges were needed to keep the tree from setting back and pinching the saw. They were also used to help push the tree in the direction you wanted it to fall. A sledge hammer was needed to pound the wedges. An old empty whiskey bottle was filled with kerosene and hung on the tree. The kerosene was poured onto the saw to help keep the pitch found in these big trees from building up on the saw and slowing the cutting action. Every logger used caulked boots. They had small spikes on the bottom of the boots making it easier to walk up and down the logs.

Fallers most often worked in pairs deciding where to fall the tree. They would chop a small notch in the tree, then put the springboard in the notch at about chest height in order to get above the swell of the tree. The swell is found at the base of the tree swelling outward where the wood is harder, the grain is wavier and contains more pitch. This portion of the tree was found unusable by the sawmills. Sometimes the fallers would go up three or four boards high. Once above the swell of the tree they would stand on the springboard, then saw and chop a face into the tree in the direction they wanted the tree to fall. Moving to the back side of the tree to start the back cut, one man pulling, one man pushing, back and forth with even strokes of power and speed. As the sawing action moved closer to the face cut a cracking sound meant the massive giant was ready to fall. The cry "Timber" could be heard, then with a roaring thunder the tree would fall making the ground shake. After a few minutes the dust and broken limbs would settle and the fallers would pick up their gear and move on to the next tree. Always on the lookout for broken limbs, known as widow makers lodged in the remaining standing trees, these limbs could be dislodged and fall on the men below. An older faller once told me "you always look up because even a small limb falling from the top of these tall trees could be fatal". These types of accidents were common and many women became widows.

The timber faller was one of the most dangerous and highest paid jobs in the logging camp. Depending on the size of the trees, a good pair of fallers could cut five to ten trees containing 50,000 to 70,000 thousand board feet of lumber each day. These men were in great shape and many worked their entire career as a timber faller.

A big spruce starts to fall, at the same time the fallers are climbing down off the springboards, the saw left on the stump. Also tents in the background were part of the Army's Spruce Division in Oregon and Washington to harvest the spruce for airplanes during WWI.

A large coastal spruce.

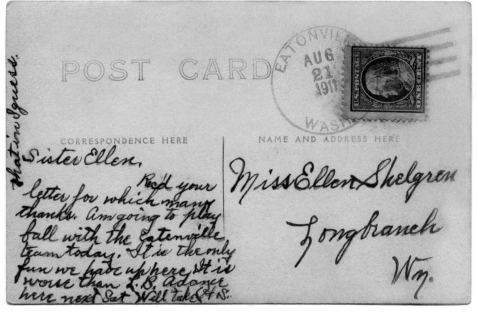

At work in Eatonville, Washington 1911.

These two postcards are of the same tree. One was found in Alaska and one was found in West Virginia.

11

Not quite finished with chopping in the face.

Native American fallers working in the big timber.

Tree so big the fallers had to side notch the tree, giving them the room needed to pull the saw.

Starting the back cut on a giant Douglas fir.

Loggers pose in face cut of a large red cedar at Gold Basin,
Washington.

Falling timber near Sultan, Washington making the back cut,
1908.

Near Marcola, Oregon standing in a virgin forest, 1908.

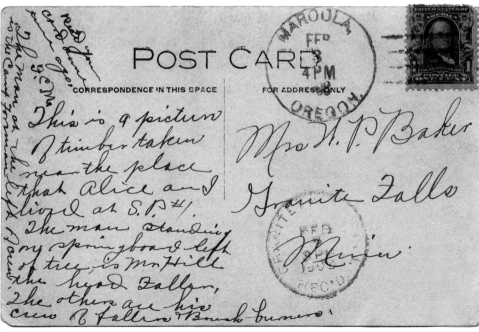

Back of card.

15

Lying in the face of a big Douglas fir. Note how close the trees
have grown together.

Chopping the face cut in a 12 foot diameter Douglas fir, Ferndale, Washington 1910. Left handed choppers were in high demand.

Loggers posing by a Spruce tree at Ferndale, Washington 1912.

Family and friends. Like most professions, sons would follow in their father's footsteps.

Logger lying in face cut of a pine tree posing for picture.

A very large Douglas fir.

Fallers and their tools.

A day in the sun.

Father and son standing by a fallen Hemlock.

Faller sitting on a massive fir log.

Fallers and their wives.

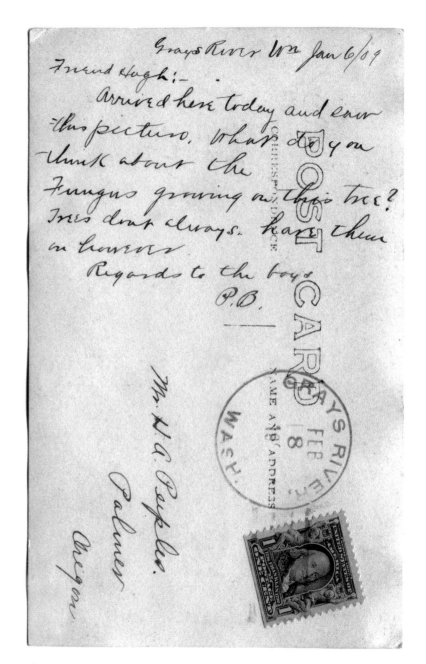

The ladies on the tree, postcard sent to Palmer, Oregon 1909. "Note the Logger's Humor" on the back of the card.

Sisters in their Sunday best near Mabel, Oregon 1908.

Ladies one board high.

Buckers

Buckers with their saws.

With the cry of "Timber" echoing through the forest, the buckers knew another tree was about to fall. Once on the ground it was the buckers job to buck or cut the tree into measured lengths of logs. Because the trees were so large and tall they had to be bucked into sections so they could be moved. Lengths were determined or set by the needs of the sawmill. Most often only the top grade wood was harvested and only the prime logs free of knots and defects would be transported to the sawmill.

Buckers worked in crews, each man bucking his own tree. More money could be made that way. Bucking these large trees was difficult work and was very dangerous. One needed to be tough as nails and strong as an ox. Logs being round liked to roll. The steeper the ground the more likely the log would roll, putting the bucker in danger. One of the first rules of thumb is never buck from the downhill side, for the log could move or roll at any time. Talking with an old timer, he told me that they did what they had to do in order to get the job done, and yes there were close calls, but you took it in stride as it was all in a days work. A days work was ten to twelve hours, six days a week.

The tool used was the bucking saw because it was wider than a falling saw, making it more rigid and stronger. The undercutter tool was a steel rod pointed on one end with a wheel in the middle. The undercutter was pounded into the side of the log, then the saw was set on the wheel with the teeth facing upward. This allowed the bucker to saw the log from the bottom up. (see page 27) Bucking wedges kept the saw from being pinched. A sledgehammer for driving in the wedges, an axe and a bottle of kerosene were also needed in the bucking process.

When all the logs were bucked, a sniping crew would bevel the ends of the log, thus enabling the log to be pulled over small objects when being yarded to the landing.

A bucker using an undercutter to help him saw in an upward direction.

Bucking on the downhill side of the log. Oak Point, Washington 1915.

Bucker using his axe handle as an undercutter tool. One less tool to carry.

Native American bucking a Douglas fir, showing off the tools of the trade.

At Camp 5 buckers starting their cut. Note how the trees were fell side by side making it easier for the buckers to do their job, 1908.

Buckers working their way down the tree.

The tree being bucked is bound up against a stump. When bucking a log that's under pressure like this, one has to be very careful for when the cut is made the pressure will be released, the log could split, roll and jerk violently. Great skill was required when bucking these logs.

Bucker standing by a fallen tree. The long pole was used for measuring the length of the logs to be cut.

Saw filer working in the woods on bucking saws, 1913.

Not finishing the cut caused the log to slab off a chunk of wood.

A big Pine tree and a nice pair of boots.

A drag saw cutting firewood from a very large Douglas fir. Bottle of kerosene above the woodcutters head.

Oxen, Horses & Mules

Oxen, Horses & Mules

Oxen ready to hook up a turn of logs.
The bullwacker having a smoke.

33

In the early years oxen, horses and mules were primarily used to pull logs from the woods to the landing, where they could be loaded and sent to the sawmill for processing. A new steam machine would soon change the way logs were yarded, making animal power obsolete. This section will focus on oxen, horses and mules and their contribution to the logging history here in the Northwest.

Oxen were large and powerful beasts; slow, but dependable. Some animals were as large as 1,800 pounds. Depending on the size of the logs, these animals could pull two to three logs at a time, which is roughly 4,000 to 8,000 board feet per trip. Each team could make two to three trips per day. The logs were chained together forming a straight line that would snake its way through the woods when being pulled. When working oxen in pairs, wooden yokes were used to hold the oxen side by side. By attaching chains to the yoke more pairs could be added, sometimes four, five and six pairs of oxen where needed. Multiple pairs were known as bull teams. Getting the most work from a team was the job of the bullwacker. Strong willed, the bullwacker had quite the vocabulary and could be heard over long distances. If you wanted to learn a few new words then just listen to the bullwacker as he was working the bull team. With a whip and a long stick, the bullwacker and his team could pull logs all day long.

The loggers took great care of their animals as a good bull team could cost $600 to $700. If a handler mistreated his team he would be let go and word spread of his deed. Shortly after the turn of the century the use of oxen was coming to an end. For that reason real photo postcards of oxen are very rare.

Horses and mules also played a vital role in the yarding and transportation of the logs. It's been said that horses were easier to work with and if handled right, they could move logs as well as oxen.

Teamsters handled the horses and mules, having many of the same attributes as that of the bullwacker. They both had a strong drive and determination, and that was to get as many logs yarded as physically possible every day and that's just what they did.

Plank and skid roads were needed for the teams to work effectively. Some of these roads were as long as two miles, built over all kinds of terrain. Skid roads were built with logs that were buried in the ground parallel to each other with just the top exposed. They were spaced far enough apart to keep the end of the log from hanging up or digging into the ground, thus allowing the logs to ride just above the forest floor when being pulled by the teams on the way to the landing. During the dry summer months large clouds of dust would billow up as the teams worked their way to the landing, sometimes making it hard to breathe.

Plank roads were used in wet or boggy areas, and were generally constructed from rough cut lumber attached to a log base making a flat surface that the logs could be hauled on. With the use of steam power being the way of the future for the logging industry, it was time to change the way the work was being done and the era of using oxen and horses to pull logs was coming to an end.

Oxen pulling logs over a skid road near Warrenton, Oregon 1908.

Oxen on a skid road, the bullwacker is holding a goad stick used to direct the animals.

Using horse power to yard logs to the landing. Note all the rigging needed.

End of the road for the oxen at the landing. The logs were rolled onto horse drawn wagons then taken to the sawmill. The oxen would then return to the forest for another turn of logs. Near Marcola, Oregon.

Ladies getting the job done working a team of horses and getting the wood out.

Teamsters posing with a large cedar log.

Resting the horses while a young boy brings drinking water to the team.

A line horse was used to take the main line or cable back into the woods so the steam donkey could pull more logs.

A load of logs arriving at a sawmill near Grants Pass, Oregon 1919.

River log drive on the Santiam 1913. River horses were used to help free up logs that were stuck.

Near Granite Falls, Washington 1911. Shake bolts hauled on a wooden sled.

Loaded wagon. Note: the long lever at the rear of the wagon is the brake.

A very large load of Cedar shake bolts making it difficult for the horses to pull.

A wagon load of Cedar shake bolts on their way to the mill. Used for roofing, cedar was in great demand near Clatskanie, Oregon.

Young boy ready to drive the team to the sawmill with a one log load.

Massive Douglas fir log being pulled by horses over a plank road.

Steam Donkey

Steam Donkey

A new steam donkey arriving at Frances, Washington 1909.

In 1882 John Dolbeer, an ex-naval engineer, invented the first steam logging machine known as a donkey. Using a boiler to create high pressure steam to turn gears that turned a spool, a rope or wire cable was wrapped around the spool, and the cable was attached to a log out in the forest. As the spool turned, the cable would slowly winch the log to the landing area. Always on the lookout for better ways to improve production and cut cost, the steam donkey seemed like a good fit. Yet early on, the loggers were somewhat skeptical of how well these new machines would hold up to the daunting task of moving these big logs from the forest to the landing. Many had a wait and see attitude. It didn't take long for the loggers to see that with the power and speed of the donkey engine it was faster and cheaper to yard and load logs, plus it was the way of the future. This meant the days of yarding logs with oxen and horses was coming to an end.

The steam donkey, with its long reach, changed the way logs would be taken from the forest. To fuel or power the donkey engine all one needed was wood for heat, water for steam and men with nerves of steel. All were plentiful here in the Northwest. Mounted on log skids carved from logs by a master axmen, the steam donkey, with its power and versatility, could pull itself using its own power over all kinds of terrain; even across small rivers. When ground logging with a steam donkey, the operator could reach out about a mile or so into the forest and drag logs back to the landing. Once the logs were at the landing they could then be loaded with the power of steam. In 1899 Bob Barr of Bridal Veil, Oregon was credited with being the first to use a high lead logging system which allowed the loggers an effective way to log the steepest of ground.

There are many different ways to high lead log but they all needed a spar tree for lift "a tree that's had its top cut out and then rigged with blocks". A cable called the main line ran from the donkey engine up to the top of the spar tree, through the block, then out to the logging area so the logs could be brought back to the landing where they would be loaded and sent to the sawmill. The steam donkey operator was called a "donkey puncher", whose job was to keep the pressure up and the logs moving. By watching the gauges and at the same time working foot and hand controls, a good operator could move a lot of logs in a day.

The donkey puncher had to be constantly aware of what was going on around him and able to react to any given situation. For communication a steam whistle was used. Mounted on the donkey engine, the whistle had a wire attached that was strung out to a point with a good view of the logging operation. Known as a "whistle punk", his job was to signal the donkey puncher by pulling the wire like Morse Code, each pull had a meaning. One whistle meant stop, two meant go ahead. These signals had to be done right or men could be hurt or killed.

There is a funny story about the first two steam donkey engines that were used by the Bridal Veil Lumber Company at the Palmer Mill site. They were hauled up the Columbia River on a steamboat to the mill town of Bridal Veil. Upon their arrival Mr. Palmer asked his woods boss to unload the two new steam engines and move them up to Larch Mountain to the new job site. Several hours later the woods boss came to Mr. Palmer and told him that he had worn out two teams of oxen and one team of horses and he still was unable to move these machines. Mr. Palmer told him to get a fire going in the boiler and build up a head of steam. The steam donkey could pull itself anywhere it needed to go! It was said that it took a week to make the climb up the mountain to the job site.

The earliest steam donkeys were flat spooled.

Willamette Iron and Steel Works at Portland, Oregon loading a new donkey engine for shipment, 1917.

Work crew building a sled for the new donkey engine to be mounted to. Sled building was an art, the finest logs were used, and all the work was done by hand.

Moving day. The horses pull the cable out so it can be tied to a tree or rock, then the steam donkey could pull itself forward along with the other wagons. This process was repeated until you got to where you were going.

The Donkey Engineer.

All in a days work.

Building a skid road using a steam donkey.

Logging on the Lewis River in Washington.

Loggers liked having their pictures taken.

Showing pride when this moment was caught in time.

Loggers pride.

Donkey engine pulling logs to the river. Many logs were floated to the sawmills.

The cook took this picture of a steam donkey moving the blacksmith shop to a new camp site. Stayton, Oregon 1909.

Moving donkey engine by railcar.

Donkey pulling itself across a steep hillside
near Long Beach, Washington.

Building a bridge. How did they get that donkey up there?

Or up there?

Accidents did happen.

Men were hurt or killed when a donkey engine tipped.

Men could be burned, scalded or crushed.

Unloading a donkey engine.

Cutting wood for the donkey engine.

Steam shovel building a railroad grade.
Everett, Washington 1911.

Back of card.

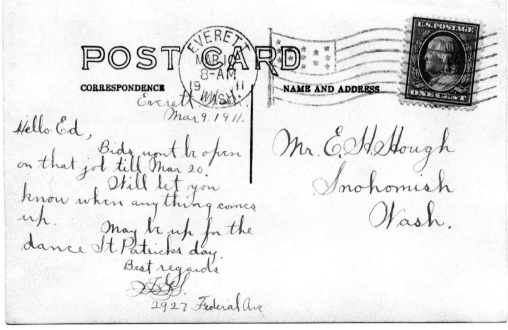

Hello Ed,
 Bids wont be open
on that job till Mar 20.
 Will let you
know when any thing comes
up.
 May be up for the
dance St. Patricks day.
 Best regards

2927 Federal Ave

Everett
Mar 9. 1911.

Mr. E. H. Hough
Snohomish
Wash.

The whole crew showed up for this photo.

Steam tractor pulling logs that contain over 12,000 board feet of lumber.

Unloading logs at the mill pond.

With a good head of steam, this tractor pulling
three wagons of logs is headed to the mill.

Yarding

Yarding

Trees that have been fell and bucked are
now ready to be yarded.

After the trees were felled and bucked the next phase was to get the logs to the landing. Moving these large logs over this rugged terrain was a daunting task that challenged a man's will all day, every day. Loggers were very creative when finding new and better ways to yard logs from the forest.

When yarding logs with a steam donkey, several methods were used. Ground logging used logging dogs: two 'L' shaped metal rods with a spike at one end that was pounded into the log, one on each side and attached to a chain, which is attached to the main line that is then pulled along the ground to the landing. High lead logging was when the logs were lifted off the ground using a spar tree for lift and by rigging a block with a cable at the top of the spar. The cable can then reach out over 1,000 feet to get a log. Pulling the choker tight like a noose meant the choker was set. The choker was attached to the main line and when the signal was given, the log would then be pulled to the landing by the steam donkey. It was the choker setters job to set the choker then find a safe place to stand, for once the signal was given and the logs started to move towards the landing, all hell would break loose.

This was fast and demanding work, so a man must be able to climb over logs, stumps, limbs and brush while carrying the choker and dragging the main line in order to set the choker. This task was most often done by the younger men. Generally a new man would start his career as a choker setter. This was also one of the lowest paying jobs in the woods. On an average day a choker setter could figure on getting bitten, stung, poked, slapped, pinched, cut, gouged, tripped, slip and fall, all in a day's work.

When yarding logs there were many dangers facing the choker setters. Being caught in the bite of the line could be fatal. This meant that when the donkey puncher got the signal to go ahead, he would open the throttle, the cable would tighten up very fast and if the choker setter was standing between the log and the cable he was in big trouble. "Hang ups" happened as the logs were being yarded in. They could hang up on stumps, rocks or downed logs causing the log to turn sideways or the choker could break, allowing the log and debris to come rolling back down the hillside toward the loggers. With just seconds to find a safe place to hide, it tested a man's courage and luck. Diving behind a big stump, while keeping a watchful eye on the rolling log was a safe place to be. Back then, as now, a good rule of thumb is "watch the old guy and do what he does".

Giant Douglas fir plowing the ground when being yarded. Beveling or sniping the edges of the log helped it to ride over objects when being yarded.

With the choker being set, the log is ready to be yarded to the landing by the steam donkey. Near Long Beach, Washington.

One of my favorite cards. Loggers holding the choker. Note the little boy standing on the log barefoot.

The Tommy Moore block allowed the rigging to be pulled through the block after the chokers were unhooked, then hooking the chokers back up to the rigging allowed the log to be turned and then pulled in a different direction.

Sitting on top of the carriage.

Riding the rigging was so very dangerous as this photo card shows.

The choker setters.

Topping a spar tree. The top going over.

A wave from the high climber letting known that he's OK.

High Lead.
Bill
150 FT
Spar Tree
Powers Ore.

Rigging the spar tree with blocks and cable.

Splicing a broken cable at Camp 3 near New Kamilche, Washington 1909.

The
Landing

The landing was an area where the logs that were being yarded from the forest were stored or loaded onto wagons, trains and trucks, which then were transported to the sawmill. Often cost would determine which method of hauling was used. The landings were built near roads, railroads, lakes and rivers. If there was a way to get the logs to the sawmill, the loggers would try it.

Early on when animals where used for yarding logs, the landing was built higher than the road or track. This way logs could be rolled into place when loading. (see page 38) Over time the steam donkey proved itself to be very well suited for loading logs and was widely used. With the power and versatility of the steam donkey, new methods were developed for loading logs. A spar tree rigged for loading gave the lift needed to raise and lower the log and at the same time swing the log into place.

When loading logs, one way was to wrap a cable around the middle of the log, finding the balance point. Then the log could be lifted and loaded. Another way was the use of loading tongs, a device made of metal that had two S shaped arms that were hinged together and used for grabbing the log so it could be lifted into place. (see page 80) End hooks are metal S shaped hooks, attached to a loading cable, one for each end of the log. By driving the hooks deep into the ends of the log this would allow for an even lift. The head loader determined which log went where, keeping in mind the load needed to be balanced so the logs would not shift during the trip to the mill. With these new loading techniques, logs could be loaded faster than ever before.

The landing was a very active place. While logs came in from the woods, logs were being loaded at the same time. Always on the lookout for problems, one needed to be ready to react to any danger in a moments notice. A cable breaking or an end hook letting loose, allowing the log to fall and roll possibly crushing a man; danger was everywhere. There was no daydreaming when working the landing.

The landing with logs being yarded in from the forest. They are loaded onto railcars and then sent to the sawmills.

Loading tongs lifting a long log.

Big logs at the landing.

Rolling a log on a horse drawn wagon.

The Boys riding the hooks for Benson Timber Company in Clatskanie, Oregon.

Marcola, Oregon. Fischer- Bros. Lumber Company.

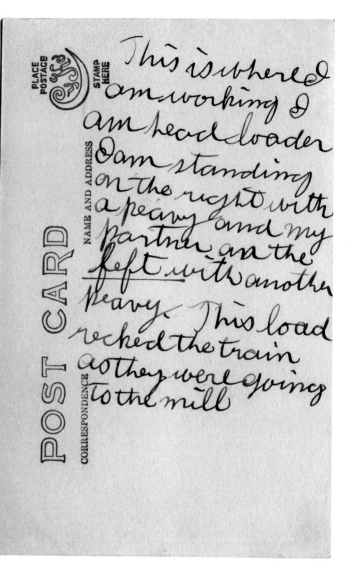

This is where I am working I am head loader I am standing on the right with a peavy and my partner on the left with another peavy. This load recked the train as they were going to the mill

Back of card.

Nicolles Camp. Loading logs near Marcola, Oregon.

Marcola, Oregon 1908.

Using end hooks to load this log. If the hooks came loose the hook tender would be in big trouble.

Wrapping a cable around the log was another way of loading logs.

Loggers posing with a large load of logs.

This massive log contains over 10,000 board
feet of lumber.

Railroading

Railroading

A Baldwin Locomotive, R.G. Balderee – Salem, Oregon.

From the turn of the century to the 1930's, trains were the workhorse of the timber industry, transporting most of the logs needed to the sawmills. Names like Baldwin, Climax, Heisler and Shay were a few of the trains used in the transportation of logs.

As the timber was being cut, the logging operation had to be moved deeper into the forest making the transporting cost go up. The use of horses and steam tractors was slow and ineffective and could not supply the mills the logs that they needed on a daily basis. Trains could haul a large number of logs over long distances allowing the sawmills to have a steady supply. The cost of building and maintaining the rail line, plus the purchasing of a locomotive was generally the biggest investment a logging company would make. When a new rail line was built it would open up vast amounts of virgin forest. The logging railroad consisted of a main line which went from the mill to the forest. Then like fingers, spur lines were built into the new stands of timber. After the trees were logged, the spur line would be abandoned, then the track would be removed and reused on the next line. Many of these old railroad spur lines were converted into roads that are still being used today.

Early trains weighed twenty to thirty tons and over the next couple of decades they became bigger and more powerful reaching sixty to eighty tons. Each rail car could haul from 10,000 to 15,000 board feet of logs. These massive locomotives must have been quite the sight with their whistles blowing when arriving at the sawmill with a large load of logs.

A 50-ton Shay pulling eighteen to twenty loaded rail cars needed a four man crew: an engineer who operated the train, a fireman who stoked the fire in the boiler, and two brakemen who inspected the train and operated the brakes. Experience and skill were needed when operating a steam locomotive loaded with logs. It's been said that no two steam engines handled the same and the engineers would have to get a feel for how the train would respond. The fireman also help the engineer by monitoring the gauges and controls, plus watching the tracks for any dangers that might be ahead. The brakemen had a very dangerous job for when the engineer whistled for brakes, the brakemen would jump from car to car turning the hand brakes on each rail car causing the train to slow, then releasing the brakes so the train could keep up its momentum. Men were lost on the trip to the sawmill.

Building a rail line at Eatonville, Washington 1913.

Back of card.

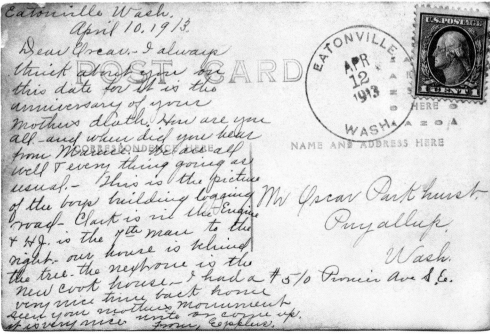

Eatonville Wash.
April 10. 1913.
Dear Oscar – I always think about you on this date for it is the anniversary of your mother's death. How are you all – and when did you hear from Warren. We are all well & every thing going as usual. – This is the picture of the boys building logging road. Clark is in the Engine & H.J. is the 9th man to the right. our house is behind the tree. the nexthouse is the new cook house. I had a very nice time back home. Seen your mothers monument it is very nice write or come up.
From, E. Plus.

Mr Oscar Parkhurst.
Puyallup.
Wash.
510 Promier Ave S.E.

91

Logging locomotive on Larch Mountain, Oregon 1910. Engineers named their trains. This one was called Peggy and was part of the Bridal Veil Lumber Company working at the Palmer Mill site.

It just so happens that this card was mailed down the street from where I live today in the small town of Latourell Falls, Oregon.

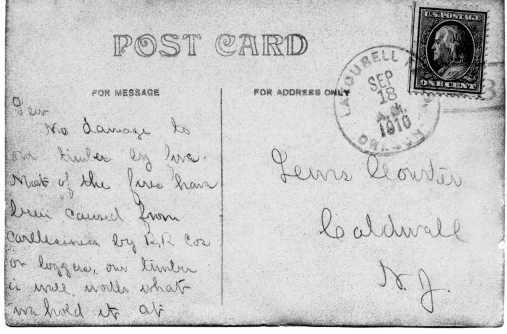

Coast Range Lumber Company at Mabel, Oregon 1913. Crew on their way to work.

Note the spark arrester on the smoke stack. This was to blow the sparks down, hoping to prevent forest fires. Rujada, Oregon 1912.

Rujada, Oregon 1912 at the water tower.

Climax Locomotive, Day Lumber Company.

West Oregon Lumber Company 1910. In 1912 the West Oregon Lumber Co. lost the engineer and firemen when the train was struck by lightening.

A Shay Locomotive at Oakville, Washington 1910. The man standing on the logs is the scaler. His job was to measure the log, then determine the board feet found in each log. Sometimes he was called the cheater.

Shay Locomotive. Pacific States Lumber Company.

Log train from Coquille to
Marshfield, Oregon.

A large Shay locomotive - Benson
Timber Co.

Wisconsin Logging and Timber Co. near Coos Bay, one man killed. Words written on the back tells what happened. "Well the logs got away from them and ran into the other load of logs and he did not hear it coming."

Great Western Lumber Co. Black Rock, Oregon.

Near Tillamook, Oregon. Highest piling bridge in the world at 172 feet.

One of the worst railroad logging accidents happened at the Seeley and Anderson Camp in Coos County, Oregon, 1912.

Seven men were killed when a new Shay locomotive pulling three railcars of logs started across the new wooden trestle a little too fast, applying the brakes causing the trestle to fall like dominos. It was said you could hear the engineer saying "boys we're gone".

Log
Trucks

Holt tractors using
gas power to haul
logs, 1914.

Looking for ways to offset the high cost of building railroads and using locomotives to transport logs to the sawmills, the use of gasoline powered machines seemed more practical and would cost less in certain cases. The Holt Manufacturing Company built one of the first tractors that used a gasoline engine which powered steel tracks that drove the machine forward. These tractors were powerful but slow and ineffective when used to haul logs over long distances. With a few changes like a blade on the front and bigger tracks, these machines were later found to be better suited for road building and pulling logs. Holt Manufacturing Co. and Best Tractor Co. formed the Caterpillar Co. when they merged in 1925.

Early log trucks however, likely got their start when some logger looking at his Model "T" Ford said "what if?" Always looking for a more efficient way to get the job done, logs were being hauled to the mills using gasoline power by 1911 or 1912. By the end of World War I there was a large surplus of military trucks and with the need to transport logs to the sawmill, many of these trucks made their way to the Pacific Northwest forests. Proving they could do the job, these early log trucks left their mark and changed the way logs would be taken to the sawmills. For almost one hundred years and with many new innovations, the log trucks are still being used today.

There were many challenges facing the truck drivers during the early days. Good roads and bridges were a major concern due to the fact that there weren't many. Tires were made of hard rubber and had no tread. This meant when it rained or snowed, the truck tires would spin and the truck would be stuck. Since the Pacific Northwest is known for its rain, the log truck driver had to find ways to deal with this common occurrence. Plank roads and wooden trestle were used throughout the region to help with this problem. There were several types of plank roads and each required large amounts of lumber to build them. With the steepness of the ground and the rough terrain, the log truck driver showed great skill and courage in maneuvering their trucks loaded with logs up and down these primitive roads.

Another major concern were the brakes (or lack of them). An old log truck driver told me you had to have "teeth in your britches when taking a load of logs down a steep canyon road. Have faith in your truck, hold on tight and do the best you can to keep her on the road, then get ready to do it all over again at the next hill". As the timber was being cut, roads moved deeper and deeper into the forest. Sometimes these massive logs were bigger than the truck! Traveling at 10 to 12 miles an hour over primitive roads had to be quite the sight to see in those early days of the log truck!

In 1920 the first truck show in the Northwest was held in Portland, Oregon. This exclusive show had 37 different makers of trucks with 65 models on display. Well known names like Ford, International and Chevrolet, plus lesser makers like Denby, Paige, Garford and Jumbo were some of the truck companies represented. C.W. Nash, of Nash Motors Co. stated that "there is no doubt as to the future of truck industry. It might almost be said that the motor truck is just beginning to come into its own". A 1920 advertisement for Traffic Motor Trucks Corporation stated that a Traffic Motor Truck could haul a 4,000 lb. load 14 miles in one hour for 30 cents worth of gasoline. One Traffic Motor Truck will do the work of three teams in one third the time with one third the help at half the cost.

1914 Packard log truck.

Gas power bringing out the logs using an N.B. Ashely Co. tractor near Issaquah, Washington.

A Kelly Springfield. Imagine driving this log down a steep hillside!

One log being hauled by two trucks. Note the driver is sitting on the hood steering, 1917.

Garford truck with a one log load.

Kelly Springfield hauling a massive spruce.

Kelly Springfield.

Bull Dog Mack truck at Enumclaw,
Washington 1918.

Bull Dog Mack truck on a ferry with a three-log load.

Mack truck at the sawmill.

Five-Ton DENBY Truck and Trailer Hauling 5,830 feet of Yellow Pine.

DENBY MOTOR TRUCK CORP.
FACTORY BRANCH
PORTLAND, OREGON
41550

Denby Motor Truck Corp. Factory branch in Portland, Oregon. A five-ton Denby truck and trailer hauling 5,830 feet of yellow pine.

At the landing where the logs were rolled up rails onto the log truck. Using a tool called a peavey, logs could be loaded by two strong men.

Two loaded trucks on a wooden trestle.

Accidents did happen. A log landed on the cab of a White truck during the loading process.

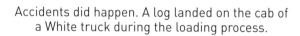

Near Sheridan, Oregon around 1920.

GMC log truck. The message on the back of this postcard said," We was going into Colville when the GMC Co. man stopped us and took our picture".

Kelly Springfield with a load of cedar shakes.

Portland, Oregon. A White truck with a big load of firewood.

No.9 SAW MILL SCENE AT PALMER   BRIDAL VEIL LUMBER MFG CO. NEAR BRIDAL VEIL ORE.

Camps & Mills

Sawmill scene at Palmer, Oregon. Large building on the left is the headquarters for the Bridal Veil Lumber Co. The row houses were for the workers and their families.

115

In the forests of the Northwest, timber was king. Men were needed to harvest the trees that would be sent to the nearby sawmill for processing into lumber. Logging camps were remote and far from the big cities. Sawmills could be found throughout the Northwest. If there was a large stream, river or lake there was probably a mill on it for cutting lumber, railroad ties and cedar shakes. Oregon and Washington led the nation in wood production.

Palmer Mill was a typical lumber mill that could be found anywhere in the northwest located on Larch Mountain in Oregon. The operation at Palmer Mill had fifty miles of railroad track which they used to haul logs for almost 50 years. Palmer Mill supplied 100,000 to 150,000 rough cut lumber that was flumed over five miles down to the planing mill at Bridal Veil, Oregon daily. The mills were built to take advantage of a new railroad line leading east along the Columbia River. This opened the way to sell their finished lumber to the east coast markets. The mill at Bridal Veil was one of the longest operating lumber mills west of the Mississippi until it closed in the late 1980's.

One big problem the mills and the camps faced was a high turn over of men in the work place. Most men after getting paid would go home to their families or go to town and blow their money on a good time and after a few days or weeks they would head back to camp. Mr. Palmer was one of the first to build houses for the workers family. He also built schools, stores and churches. Both towns of Palmer Mill and Bridal Veil were self-contained communities. Soon the workers brought their families with them and production went up. The school at Palmer, Oregon was one of the earliest rural schools to have electric lights, circa 1916.

Camps varied in size from ten to twenty men found in a small camps, to several hundred men in the larger camps. Life in the camps started at 4:00 a.m. The men would have breakfast which consisted of flapjacks, pork and coffee. The average logger needed from 8,000 to 9,000 calories of food per day in order to do their job. When the bull buck or boss called "all out for the woods" this meant it was time to load up and head to the job site. After a long hard days work the men headed back to camp, cleaned up and had chow. At the bunkhouse the men could be found playing cards. Storytelling was a fun past time. Stories of the biggest trees, the steepest ground, coldest winters, every man had a story to tell. As the kerosene lamps were turned off, the loggers would call it day. Most camps were dry camps, no alcohol allowed. It was easier to keep the peace that way. With the loggers constantly on the move, camps that had good food and housing would have a better chance of keeping the men in camp. Many of these camps and mills grew into towns as others faded away.

During World War I, the United States of America felt the way to win the war was through the air. The Sitka Spruce tree of the Pacific Coast produced wood that was strong, straight grained and lightweight that was perfect for building airplanes. In 1917 the Spruce Production Division was formed to help in the harvest of these trees so planes could be built. The camps themselves were clean and well kept, good food and fresh bedding was well received by the loggers. With the war ending many of the camps never reached full production.

The town of new Palmer built after the 1902 fire. Note the dead trees in the background were from this fire.

Winter scene at Palmer. The log deck in the background has two to three million board feet of logs ready to be cut.

Workers housing at Palmer, Oregon.

Mill workers home at Palmer, Oregon 1910.

Typical homes for families. These houses allowed the workers and their families to stay together while working at the camps.

Bridal Veil logging camp at Palmer, Oregon.
One of the three trains used to haul logs.

Palmer Flume near a homestead on
Larch Mt., Oregon.

Flume used to send rough cut lumber from Palmer to the planing mill at
Bridal Veil, Oregon.

Birds eye view of the mill and town at Bridal Veil, Oregon. The Columbia River is in the background.

Typical bunkhouse that was the loggers home when living in the camps. Note the straw bedding.

Mess hall. Cooks serving the men.

Workers ready to head out to the logging site.

Cooks at the mess hall. A load of log on its way to the sawmill.

Building bunkhouses on railcars so they could be moved to other camp sites.

Bunkhouses at new location.

Coastal sawmill.

Sawmill at Wendling, Oregon 1923.

Albany Commercial Club visiting Hammond Lumber Co. camps in Mill City, Oregon.

Sawmill near Winlock, Washington. Note how narrow the canyon is. Sites like this made it easy to build dams. The water was used to power the sawmill.

Cedar shake bolts ready to be hauled to the mill.

Shingle mill at Duvall, Washington.
Hauling shake bolts to the mill.

Shingle mill at Duvall, Washington. Packing the cedar shake for shipment.

Shingle mill at Duvall, Washington. Cedar shakes ready for shipment.

Saw filer preparing a saw for the next days work. An old saw filer told me
"that he would go into the woods and watch the men pulling the saws
through the logs and then file the saw to match the motions of each man."

Millworkers at the Ingersoll Shingle MFG Co.
Shelton, Washington.

The scaler and his tools; used to measure the logs. One would measure the diameter of the log and the other would measure the length. This would help him determine the board feet found in each log.

During World War I the U.S. Army sent men into the forest of the Pacific Northwest to help harvest the coastal spruce so it could be used in the manufacturing of airplanes needed to win the war. All trees marked with an X were to be cut and used for airplane production.

Only the prime wood (clear, tight grain wood with no knots) could be used for the planes. Horses pulling a slab of prime wood to the landing. Tillamook, Oregon.

Once at the landing the slabs would be loaded onto a log truck then taken to the rail yard. Tillamook, Oregon.

133

Once at the rail yard the slabs were loaded onto rail cars. Tillamook, Oregon.

A SIGNAL CORPS UNITED STATES ARMY locomotive arriving at Toledo, Oregon with a nice load of spruce logs.

One of the many spur lines used by the Spruce Division during this time. The train was hauling a steam donkey to a new work site.

Loggers at play splitting a spruce log in thirty minutes at Seaside, Oregon.

Spruce camp and mill at Tillamook, Oregon.

447 Squadron at Tillamook, Oregon.

Spruce Camp 1E near Seaside, Oregon.

U.S. Spruce Workers Hotel at Garibaldi, Oregon.

Spruce Camp 1C in Clatsop, Oregon.

Always time for getting your photo taken.

Murphy's Camp in Clatsop County, Oregon.

Spruce Camp 1F in Clatsop, Oregon.

Large Douglas fir makes for a good photo.

Early timber festival.

Loggers & Their Dogs

Loggers &
Their Dogs

The old saying "Dogs are mans best friend" surely is true when it comes to the logger. After viewing thousands of logging postcards, one cannot help but notice that the loggers loved their dogs. The number of photos taken with dogs in them tell us that there was a strong bond between them. These photo cards of the loggers and their dogs shows us that dogs were also at the work place. I can say things have not changed much for every logger I know has dogs and many take them to work. If you were to ask a logger if his dog was part of the family he would most likely say "you bet".

Rujada, Oregon.

Note both photos are of the same crew and dog. These photos must have been taken on the same day. Photo cards purchased at two different locations.

147

The next generation.

Done for the day!

Bibliography

Glory Days of LOGGING
By RALPH W. ANDERSON
Superior Publishing

TIMBER
By RALPH W. ANDERSON
Schiffer Publishing

This Was LOGGING
By RALPH W. ANDERSON
Superior Publishing

Logging Railroads of the West
By Kramer Adams
Superior Publishing

WHEN TIMBER STOOD TALL
By JOSEPH H. PIERRE
Superior Publishing

BRING OUT THE BIG ONES
By WALT WENTZ
Oregon Forest Products Transportation
Association

BIG TIMBER BIG MEN
By CAROL J. LIND
Hancock House Publishing LTD

IN SEARCH OF STEAM DONKEY
By MERV JOHNSON
TIMBER TIMES

LOGGER
By the Editors of Time Life Books

The History of the Bridal Lumber Company
By Bill Carr

This Was Trucking
By Robert F. Karolevitz
BONANZA BOOKS

Sunday Oregonian Feb. 22, 1920
By L.H. Gregory
Pages 2 and 9

Pacific Spruce Corporation
Lumber World Review 1924

Living East of the Sandy
Volume 1
By Clarence E. Mershon

North American's Investment Guide
to Real Photo Post Cards

Author

Moving to the Pacific Northwest at an early age, it didn't take long to fall in love with the beauty and the uniqueness of this part of our country. With its forests, mountains, valleys, oceans, rivers, and deserts, the Northwest has it all. For a young boy life was great!

Upon graduating from Corbett High School I joined the U.S. Marine Corp. After completing my tour of duty I came home and tried my hand at several jobs. Hearing about the loggers way of life always fascinated me and having the desire to be outdoors logging seemed the way to go. I started a small logging company, bought my first chain saw and rented a Cat to fall trees and clear brush so the land could be reforested by planting Douglas fir. Most of my time was spent falling and bucking trees. Between jobs cutting firewood, splitting cedar shake bolts and planting trees kept a man busy. For over 20 years working hard, facing the challenges that each day brought and getting the job done gave me great pride knowing I was part of a long and proud tradition. I was very fortunate to have worked with some of the best.

Having a passion for history led me to learn all I could about the industry I had become a part of. Talking with any old timer who would share their story, visiting old logging sites, plus reading numerous logging books, I got a better understanding of what it meant to be a logger.

My hobbies include part time history detective, sharing history from logging and lumbering, fishing on the Columbia River and farming with local school kids, tourists and other historical groups, also rock hounding and looking at old photos.

My hope is to preserve these heritages for future generations.